Happy Birthday Jesus

Nell Navillus

Illustrated by

Jodie McCallum

FaithP★int
PRESS

Happy Birthday Jesus
Copyright © 2007 by Cliff Road Books, Inc.
Produced by arrangement with FaithPoint Press

ISBN-13: 978-1-58173-703-5
ISBN-10: 1-58173-703-3

Printed in China

Happy Birthday Jesus

Long ago, in the town of Bethlehem, in the land of Judea, there was a very special birthday party.

The day was December 25th. On that cold night, in a stable surrounded by friendly animals, Mary and her husband, Joseph, prepared to have a baby. The stable was the only place left to stay because so many people were visiting Bethlehem.

But the stable was warm, and the animals kept a close watch on the young family. When the baby was born, a beautiful light appeared around him. The animals pricked up their ears. Mary smiled. "Listen!" she said to Joseph. "You can hear the angels singing!"

The night sky was filled with the glory of angel voices.
They were rejoicing because Mary's new baby, Jesus,
had been born. He was a very special baby, the Son
of God. He brought to all people the promise of
eternal life.

"I'm giving the Baby Jesus my manger to use as a bed,"
said the donkey.
"I'm giving him my milk," said the cow.
"I'm giving my eggs," said the chicken.
"I'm giving my wool to keep Jesus warm,"
said the sheep.

Just then some visitors arrived for the birthday party. It was a group of shepherds, who had been called by the voices of the angels to come to the stable in Bethlehem. The shepherds fell to their knees. Their leader said, "We are here to worship the newborn king." And he gave Mary and Joseph a lamb.

Then they were joined by three wise men who had traveled very far to find the special new baby. "We followed the star in the east," the wise kings told Mary and Joseph.

They presented Jesus with precious gifts of gold, and spices called frankincense and myrrh that were usually only owned by kings.

It was quite a birthday party Jesus had that night.

But there was one guest who hadn't brought anything for Jesus. A little shepherd boy had been tending sheep with his father in the fields, and came shyly to the stable to watch the birthday party. He peeked out from behind his father's robes at the rejoicing and celebration.

But the shepherd boy was sad. He could see the beautiful baby in the manger, and the love in the eyes of Mary, Joseph, the wise kings, the shepherds, and the friendly animals. They had all given Jesus wonderful gifts. But the little shepherd boy had no gift to give.

He pulled on his father's robe. He pulled again, and again. Finally his father looked down. "What's wrong, son?" his father asked, as he saw the tear in his son's eye. "I have no gift for the baby," the boy said.

The shepherd boy's father smiled and picked him up in his arms. He hugged him tightly and kissed him on the cheek. The boy smiled through his tears. "Son," said the father, "you can always give this, the most precious gift of all."

"I can give a hug?" asked the little shepherd boy.
"Yes, son. The very best gift of all is your love."

So the little shepherd boy quietly crept close to the manger, his eyes shining. Mary smiled and gave a nod, and the shepherd boy gave baby Jesus a big hug and whispered, "I love you, Baby Jesus."

And then the angels really did sing, for it was the most beautiful and blessed birthday party of all.